Contents

Welcome to

Sight Word Tales

These cheerful stories teach the top 100 sight words—long recognized as the most important words to learn in order to ensure early reading success. What are sight words? Reading research shows that 50 to 75 percent of text is made up of common, repeated words. Knowing these words by sight—that is, being able to recognize them immediately and without thought—greatly increases reading fluency and comprehension. The *Sight Word Tales* collection includes the 100 most frequently repeated words children are likely to encounter in their reading material.

So why take the time to teach your child sight words? Consider these two sentences:

We like to read. *Some books are very good.*

It's likely that you were able to take in the meaning of each sentence as a whole, simply because words such as *we, like, to, some, are, very,* and *good* are so familiar that they barely require a glance to convey meaning. As mature readers, we may take this lightning-fast process for granted. But to a child who is just beginning to read, these sentences look quite different. Children who need to analyze each letter in order to decode the words *we, like,* and *to* may have already forgotten their meaning by the time they get to the word *read.* In order to comprehend the sentence, they would then need to go back to the beginning and read it a second time. Now imagine going on to the next sentence and going through the same process all over again. How likely is it that you would remember the first sentence once you'd deciphered the second?

Sight Word Tales

New York • Toronto • London • Auckland • Sydney
Mexico City • New Delhi • Hong Kong • Buenos Aires

Cover designed by Michelle H. Kim
Interior designed by Grafica, Inc.

ISBN: 978-1-338-11699-1
Copyright © by Scholastic Inc.
All rights reserved. Printed in China.

1 2 3 4 5 6 7 8 9 10   157   22 21 20 19 18 17 16

It's clear that learning sight words—also called *high-frequency words*—is essential to reading agility. The ability to recognize a word immediately is called *automaticity*, and it is particularly important in English because many of the most commonly repeated words do not follow regular phonetic rules. Of course, phonics is an indispensable part of any balanced literacy program, but words such as *come, would,* and *what* cannot be reliably decoded and therefore require memorization.

Research has shown that merely relying on context and exposure to language, hoping children will simply "pick up" sight words at their own pace, is a losing strategy. Sight words must be taught directly. On the other hand, studying and memorizing lists of words is unlikely to engage children. That's where *Sight Word Tales* comes in! With this collection, you get the best of both worlds—an opportunity to provide easy sight word instruction while addressing meaning, context, and a youngster's natural need for fun. So share these *Sight Word Tales* with your child…and open the door to reading success!

Happy learning,

The Editors

Tips for Sharing *Sight Word Tales*

The *Sight Word Tales* in this collection introduce sight vocabulary in such a fun way that they're sure to become a favorite part of your child's read-aloud library. Here are a few tips for helping your child get the most out of each story:

Before Reading

- Explore the "cover" page of each story and read the title aloud. Invite your child to use the title and illustration to make predictions about the story. For instance, when sharing *Come to the Zany Zoo*, you might ask: "What is unusual about the animal on the cover? What other kinds of animals do you think you might see at a zany zoo?" Thoughtful questions such as these will boost your child's comprehension skills.

- Introduce the four sight words shown in the upper right corner of the "cover" page such as *come, to, see,* and *the*. Read each word aloud as you point to it. Tell your child that these are sight words—words they can learn to recognize just by looking at them, without having to sound them out. Explain to your child that these important words will be repeated again and again in the story and that they will appear in boldface type.

- Skim through the story, encouraging your child to point out a few of the boldface sight words. Read the words aloud, inviting him or her to echo-read them after you.

During Reading

- On your first reading of the story, read it aloud— straight through—just for pleasure. Invite your child to look at the illustrations as he or she becomes engaged in the story and language.

- The next time you read the story, encourage your child to be on the lookout for the four target sight words. Invite your child to signal whenever the words are read with a clap or thumbs-up.

- On a subsequent reading, pause to read aloud the blurb that appears on the first page of the story. Encourage your child to try to spot the target sight words in the speech bubbles as well as within the illustrations. For instance, in the story *Let's Make Soup Together*, the sight word *take* is printed on a poster on the wall (page 347). In the story *All Puffins Just Love Muffins*, the sight word *just* appears on the cover of a cookbook (page 268).

- Once you've read the story several times, encourage your child to read along on words they know, particularly the targeted sight words. When you come to one, take a pause as you point to it, giving your child ample time to chime in.

After Reading

- Invite your child to make comments and ask questions related to the story. You can spark ideas with questions such as: "What was your favorite illustration? What part of the story surprised you? Who was your favorite character?" and so on. Asking meaningful questions will help to boost your child's reading comprehension skills.

- Use the review at the end of each story to gauge your child's grasp of the four target sight words. Point to each word at random, inviting him or her to read it aloud. If your child is having trouble, provide hints about the words, such as the shape of the letters, the beginning or ending sound, and so on. In addition, invite your child to complete the sentence fill-in activity. Read aloud the words in the word box, and then read aloud each sentence, challenging your child to choose the word that best fits the blank.

- To celebrate your child's sight word learning, enjoy the cheer on the last page of each story. For added fun, make a mini-megaphone out of rolled up paper and invite your child to shout it out!

- You can delve even deeper into each sight word by playing quick games that focus on word construction. For instance, when learning the word *well*, invite your child to name words that rhyme *(bell, tell, fell)*. When learning the word *stop*, encourage him or her to come up with words that begin with the same blend *(stick, stamp, stay)*.

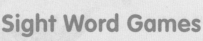

Sight Word Games

Here are a few quick and easy ideas to give your child more practice with the sight words in this collection.

Shaving-Cream Spelling

Tactile learners will benefit from sensory writing experiences. Squirt shaving cream onto a cookie sheet and have your child write sight words in the cream using a finger. Mistakes can be "erased" by smoothing the shaving cream over with a palm.

Sight Word Scavenger Hunt

Provide a list of target sight words, a stack of old magazines, a sheet of construction paper, scissors, and glue. Then challenge your child to hunt through the magazines for the words on the list, cut them out, and glue them to the construction paper. Hang your child's completed artwork on the refrigerator to reinforce sight word learning.

Silly Sentences

Write some or all of the sight words on slips of paper and place them in a bag. Then invite your child to draw three—or more—words from the bag and make a sentence. For instance, if he or she draws *want*, *jump*, and *funny*, the sentence might be: *We want to jump like funny frogs.* Copy—and collect—the sentences in a notebook, using a different color marker for each of the target words.

Go Fish

Create a deck of cards by writing 26 sight words on separate index cards. Write each word twice on each card, and cut the cards in half to make a deck of 52 cards. Each player gets five cards, and the remaining cards are placed facedown in the middle. The first player chooses a word from his or her hand and asks another player for the matching word card. If the player has the card, he or she hands it over. If not, that player says, "Go fish," and the first player picks the top card from the middle deck. If the drawn card makes a pair, the player places the pair on the table. If not, the player keeps the card and it is the next player's turn. Play continues until one player runs out of cards or the middle deck is used up.

Sight Word Tales™

can we
get no

Can We Get a Pet?

by Maria Fleming

illustrated by Amy Wummer

Sight Words

Sight words are words that you see again and again when you read. This story is filled with the sight words **can**, **we**, **get**, and **no**. Look for them in the text. Check the pictures, too!

Can we get a snake?
No!

Can we get a rat?
No!

Can we get a monkey?
No!

Can we get a bat?
No!

Can we get a raccoon?
No!

Can we get a goose?
No!

Can we get a beaver?
No!

Can we get a moose?
No!

Can we get a goat?
No!

Can we get a frog?
No!

Can we get a skunk?
No!

Can we get a dog?
Okay.
Okay? HOORAY!

Sight Word Review

Do you know the four sight words in this story?
Read aloud the word on each bone.

Sight Word Fill-ins

can	we
get	no

Listen to the sentences. Then choose a sight word from the box to fill in each blank.

> **Word Box** can we get no

1 After dinner, _____ can have ice cream!

2 Did you _____ wet in the rain?

3 There are _____ cookies left.

4 She _____ hit a ball.

5 Let's _____ a book from the library.

6 I have _____ pets.

7 Yes, _____ are going to the party.

8 I _____ ride a bike!

Sight Word Cheers

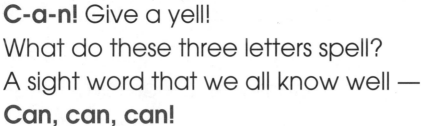

Celebrate the new sight words you learned by saying these four short cheers.

C-a-n! Give a yell!
What do these three letters spell?
A sight word that we all know well —
Can, can, can!

W-e! Give a yell!
What do these two letters spell?
A sight word that we all know well —
We, we, we!

G-e-t! Give a yell!
What do these three letters spell?
A sight word that we all know well —
Get, get, get!

N-o! Give a yell!
What do these two letters spell?
A sight word that we all know well —
No, no, no!

Come to the Zany Zoo

by Jane Quinn
illustrated by Jim Paillot

Sight Words

Sight words are words that you see again and again when you read. This story is filled with the sight words **come**, **to**, **the**, and **see**. Look for them in the text. Check the pictures, too!

Come to the zany zoo!
Come see the polka-dot kangaroo!

Come to the zany zoo!
Come see the hippo in a tutu!

Come to the zany zoo!
Come see the flamingo in one pink shoe!

Come to the zany zoo!
Come see the elephant in a canoe!

Come to the zany zoo!
Come see the panda play a peek-a-boo!

Come to the zany zoo!
Come see the leopard play a kazoo!

Come to the zany zoo!
Come see the bear make things with glue!

Come to the zany zoo!
Come see the alligator add two plus two!

Come to the zany zoo!
Come see the tiger who only says, "Moo!"

Come to the zany zoo!
Come see the zebra who is red, white, and blue!

Come to the zany zoo!
Come see the lion with a fancy hairdo!

Come to the zany zoo!
Come see the animals.
They want **to see** you!

Sight Word Review

Do you know the four sight words in this story? Read aloud the word on each shoe.

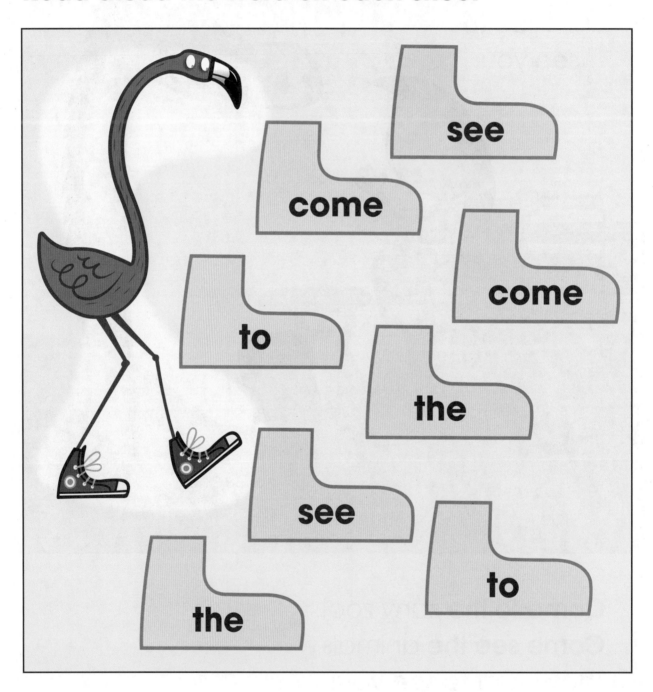

38

Sight Word Fill-ins

come to
the see

Listen to the sentences. Then choose a sight word from the box to fill in each blank.

Word Box	come	to	the	see

1 Can I _____ with you?

2 He will _____ his aunt next week.

3 The teacher told us not _____ run.

4 She cannot _____ over today.

5 I will be a fairy in _____ play.

6 Did you _____ that big bug?

7 We love _____ have picnics.

8 Let's go on _____ swings.

Sight Word Cheers

Celebrate the new sight words you learned by saying these four short cheers.

C-o-m-e! Give a yell!
What do these four letters spell?
A sight word that we all know well —
Come, come, come!

T-o! Give a yell!
What do these two letters spell?
A sight word that we all know well —
To, to, to!

T-h-e! Give a yell!
What do these three letters spell?
A sight word that we all know well —
The, the, the!

S-e-e! Give a yell!
What do these three letters spell?
A sight word that we all know well —
See, see, see!

Sight Word Tales ™

A House for Mouse

by Maria Fleming

illustrated by Tammie Lyon

Sight Words

Sight words are words that you see again and again when you read. This story is filled with the sight words **this**, **is**, **too**, and **for**. Look for them in the text. Check the pictures, too!

Mouse needs a house.
This house **is too** big **for** Mouse.

This house **is too** small.

This house **is too** round **for** Mouse.

This house **is too** tall.

This house **is too** loud **for** Mouse.

This house **is too** hairy.

This house **is too** hot **for** Mouse.

Come to the zany zoo!
Come see the alligator add two plus two!

Come to the zany zoo!
Come see the tiger who only says, "Moo!"

Come to the zany zoo!
Come see the zebra who is red, white, and blue!

Come to the zany zoo!
Come see the lion with a fancy hairdo!

Come to the zany zoo!
Come see the animals.
They want **to see** you!

Sight Word Review

Do you know the four sight words in this story?
Read aloud the word on each shoe.

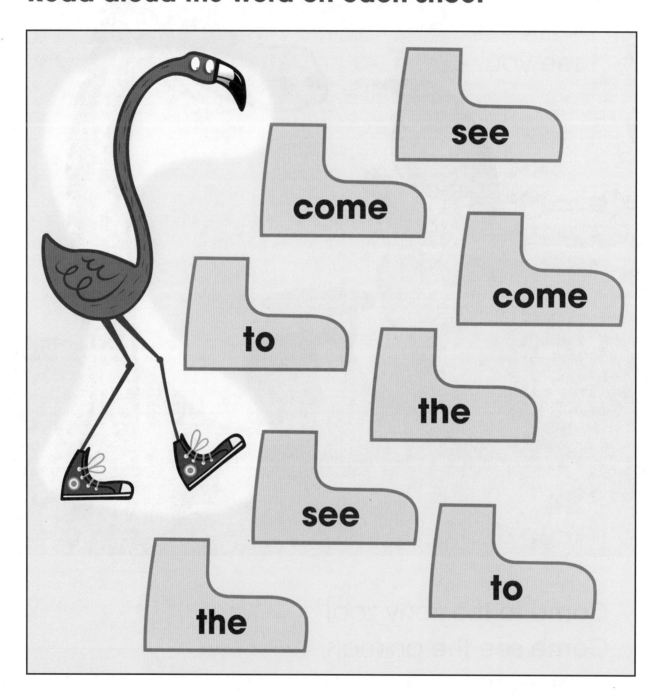

38

Sight Word Fill-ins

Listen to the sentences. Then choose a sight word from the box to fill in each blank.

| Word Box | come | to | the | see |

1 Can I _____ with you?

2 He will _____ his aunt next week.

3 The teacher told us not _____ run.

4 She cannot _____ over today.

5 I will be a fairy in _____ play.

6 Did you _____ that big bug?

7 We love _____ have picnics.

8 Let's go on _____ swings.

Answers: 1. come 2. see 3. to 4. come 5. the 6. see 7. to 8. the

Sight Word Cheers

Celebrate the new sight words you learned by saying these four short cheers.

C-o-m-e! Give a yell!
What do these four letters spell?
A sight word that we all know well —
Come, come, come!

T-o! Give a yell!
What do these two letters spell?
A sight word that we all know well —
To, to, to!

T-h-e! Give a yell!
What do these three letters spell?
A sight word that we all know well —
The, the, the!

S-e-e! Give a yell!
What do these three letters spell?
A sight word that we all know well —
See, see, see!

Sight Word Tales™

A House for Mouse

by Maria Fleming
illustrated by Tammie Lyon

Sight Words

Sight words are words that you see
again and again when you read.
This story is filled with the sight words
this, **is**, **too**, and **for**. Look for them in
the text. Check the pictures, too!

Mouse needs a house.
This house **is too** big **for** Mouse.

This house **is too** small.

This house **is too** round **for** Mouse.

This house **is too** tall.

This house **is too** loud **for** Mouse.

This house **is too** hairy.

This house **is too** hot **for** Mouse.

This house **is too** scary.

This house **is too** cold **for** Mouse.

This house **is too** bright.

This house **is too** wet **for** Mouse.

This house **is** just right!

Sight Word Review

Do you know the four sight words in this story?
Read aloud the word on each brick.

this

too   for   is

for   too

is   this

54

Sight Word Fill-ins

Listen to the sentences. Then choose a sight word from the box to fill in each blank.

Word Box	**this**	**is**	**too**	**for**

1 We had pizza _____ lunch.

2 My mom made me _____ hat.

3 I was _____ sick to go.

4 These books are _____ you.

5 My favorite snack _____ popcorn.

6 What is _____ mouse doing in my room?

7 He _____ my friend.

8 It was _____ cold to swim.

Sight Word Cheers

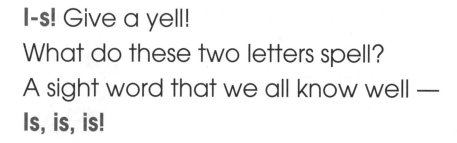

this	is
too	for

Celebrate the four new sight words you learned by saying these short cheers.

T-h-i-s! Give a yell!
What do these four letters spell?
A sight word that we all know well —
This, this, this!

I-s! Give a yell!
What do these two letters spell?
A sight word that we all know well —
Is, is, is!

T-o-o! Give a yell!
What do these three letters spell?
A sight word that we all know well —
Too, too, too!

F-o-r! Give a yell!
What do these three letters spell?
A sight word that we all know well —
For, for, for!

Sight Word Tales ™

look at
that go

Look at That Cat!

by Maria Fleming

illustrated by Patrick Girouard

Sight Words

Sight words are words that you see again and again when you read. This story is filled with the sight words **look**, **at**, **that**, and **go**. Look for them in the text. Check the pictures, too!

Look at that cat run!
Go, cat, **go**!

Look at that cat throw!
Go, cat, **go**!

Look at that cat swim!
Go, cat, **go**!

Look at that cat row!
Go, cat, **go**!

Look at that cat lift!
Go, cat, **go**!

Look at that cat ride!
Go, cat, go!

Look at that cat fly!
Go, cat, **go**

Look at that cat slide!
Go, cat, **go**!

Look at that cat skate!
Go, cat, **go**!

Look at that cat leap!
Go, cat, **go**!

Look at that cat kick!
Go, cat, **go**!

Look at that cat sleep!
It was only a dream! Oh, cat!

Sight Word Review

Do you know the four sight words in this story?
Read aloud the word on each medal.

Sight Word Fill-ins

Listen to the sentences. Then choose a sight word from the box to fill in each blank.

Word Box	look	at	that	go

1 I left my book _____ home.

2 I _____ like my twin sister.

3 Did you _____ to the park?

4 He wants _____ dog.

5 You _____ sleepy today.

6 Let's _____ to the movies.

7 We saw a tiger _____ the zoo.

8 I do not like _____ hat.

Answers: 1. at 2. look 3. go 4. that 5. look 6. go 7. at 8. that

Sight Word Cheers

Celebrate the new sight words you learned by saying these four short cheers.

L-o-o-k! Give a yell!
What do these four letters spell?
A sight word that we all know well —
Look, look, look!

A-t! Give a yell!
What do these two letters spell?
A sight word that we all know well —
At, at, at!

T-h-a-t! Give a yell!
What do these four letters spell?
A sight word that we all know well —
That, that, that!

G-o! Give a yell!
What do these two letters spell?
A sight word that we all know well —
Go, go, go!

Sight Word Tales™

My Dragon and I

by Maria Fleming
illustrated by Mike Gordon

Sight Words

Sight words are words that you see again and again when you read. This story is filled with the sight words **my**, **and**, **I**, and **like**. Look for them in the text. Check the pictures, too!

My dragon **and I like** to swing.

My dragon **and I like** to slide.

My dragon **and I like** to hop.

My dragon and I like to hide.

My dragon **and I like** to climb.

My dragon **and I like** to splash.

My dragon **and I like** to dig.

My dragon **and I like** to crash.

My dragon **and I like** to read.

My dragon **and I like** to pretend.

My dragon and I like to paint.

My dragon is **my** best friend.

Sight Word Review

my and
I like

Do you know the four sight words in this story? Read aloud the word on each puddle.

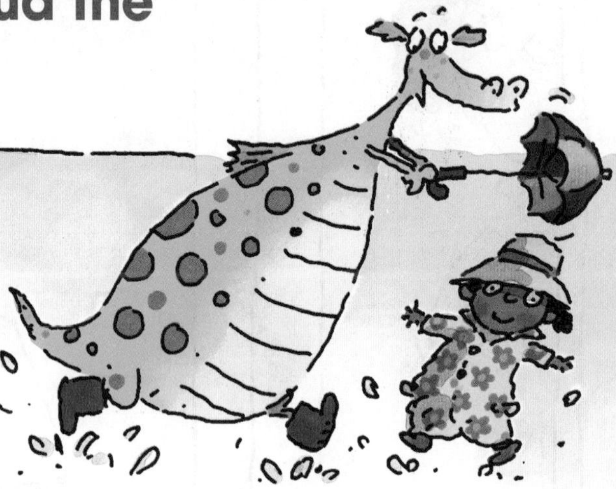

my

I

and

like

I

my

like

and

Sight Word Fill-ins

my	and
I	like

Listen to the sentences. Then choose a sight word from the box to fill in each blank.

> **Word Box**   my   and   I   like

1 _____ have a cold.

2 We _____ to play games.

3 That is _____ pencil.

4 He had a peanut butter _____ jelly sandwich.

5 Do you _____ this book?

6 _____ won the race!

7 She has a brother _____ a sister.

8 Oh no, _____ tooth fell out!

87

Sight Word Cheers

Celebrate the new sight words you learned by saying these four short cheers.

M-y! Give a yell!
What do these two letters spell?
A sight word that we all know well —
My, my, my!

A-n-d! Give a yell!
What do these three letters spell?
A sight word that we all know well —
And, and, and!

I! Give a yell!
What does this one letter spell?
A sight word that we all know well —
I, I, I!

L-i-k-e! Give a yell!
What do these four letters spell?
A sight word that we all know well —
Like, like, like!

Oodles of Noodles

by Mickey Daniels
illustrated by Kelly Kennedy

I ♥ NOODLES

Sight Words

Sight words are words that you see again and again when you read. This story is filled with the sight words **he, put, on,** and **of.** Look for them in the text. Check the pictures, too!

There once was a boy who **put** noodles **on** everything **he** ate. Oodles **of** noodles!

He put noodles **on** waffles.
Oodles **of** noodles!

He **put** noodles **on** sandwiches.
Oodles **of** noodles!

He put noodles on hot dogs.
Oodles of noodles!

He **put** noodles **on** cake.

Oodles **of** noodles!

He put noodles **on** pizza.
Oodles **of** noodles!

He put noodles on ice cream.
Oodles of noodles!

He put noodles **on** toast.
Oodles **of** noodles!

He even **put** noodles **on** noodles!
Oodles **of** noodles!

Then one day, **he** got tired **of** noodles.

Now **he puts** pickles **on** everything.
Piles **of** pickles!

Do you know the four sight words in this story?
Read aloud the word on each plate.

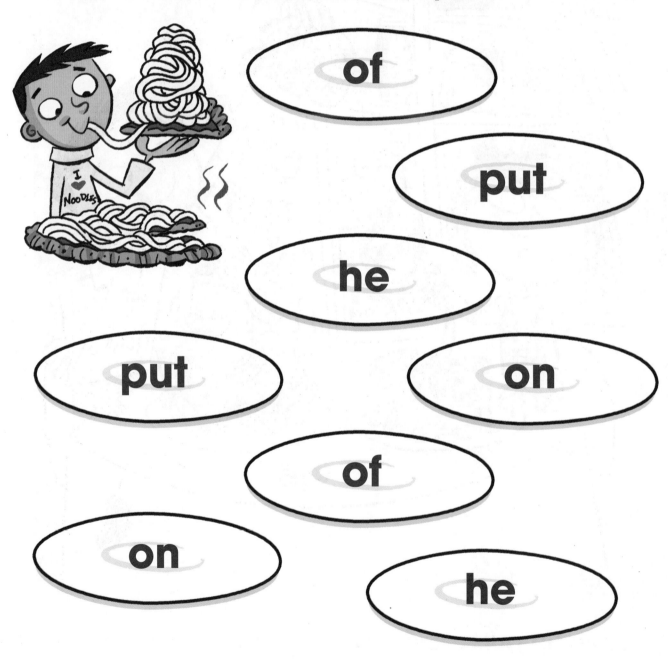

Sight Word Fill-ins

Listen to the sentences. Then choose a sight word from the box to fill in each blank.

Word Box	he	put	on	of

1 The cat is _____ the chair.

2 Where did you _____ your shoes?

3 She has a lot _____ freckles.

4 I like pepperoni _____ my pizza.

5 Is _____ your uncle?

6 We won three _____ the four games.

7 Please _____ away your toys.

8 Will _____ help us?

Sight Word Cheers

Celebrate the new sight words you learned by saying these four short cheers.

H-e! Give a yell!
What do these two letters spell?
A sight word that we all know well —
He, he, he!

P-u-t! Give a yell!
What do these three letters spell?
A sight word that we all know well —
Put, put, put!

O-n! Give a yell!
What do these two letters spell?
A sight word that we all know well —
On, on, on!

O-f! Give a yell!
What do these two letters spell?
A sight word that we all know well —
Of, of, of!

The Fix-It-Up Fairy

by Catherine Bittner

illustrated by Richard Torrey

Sight Words

Sight words are words that you see again and again when you read. This story is filled with the sight words **she**, **will**, **it**, and **up**. Look for them in the text. Check the pictures, too!

The fix-**it-up** fairy **will** fix anything!
Will she fix this doll?

She will fix **it** right **up**!

Will she fix this bear?

She will fix **it** right **up**! Oops!

Will she fix this truck?

She will fix **it** right **up**! Oh, dear!

Will she fix this bike?

She will fix **it** right **up**! Yikes!

Will she fix this wand?
She will. . . call a friend.

And her friend **will** fix **it** right **up**!

Hooray for the fix-**it-up** fairy!

Hooray for the fix-**it-up** fairy's friend!

Sight Word Review

Do you know the four sight words in this story?
Read aloud the word on each star.

she

it

will

up

she

up

it

will

118

Sight Word Fill-ins

she will
it up

Listen to the sentences. Then choose a sight word from the box to fill in each blank.

Word Box	she	will	it	up

1. The cat climbed _____ the tree.

2. The bus _____ come soon.

3. When is _____ going to the party?

4. We walked _____ a big hill.

5. Can you fix _____?

6. My dad _____ take us to school.

7. I think _____ might rain today.

8. Is _____ your big sister?

Sight Word Cheers

**Celebrate the new sight words
you learned by saying these
four short cheers.**

S-h-e! Give a yell!
What do these three letters spell?
A sight word that we all know well —
She, she, she!

W-i-l-l! Give a yell!
What do these four letters spell?
A sight word that we all know well —
Will, will, will!

I-t! Give a yell!
What do these two letters spell?
A sight word that we all know well —
It, it, it!

U-p! Give a yell!
What do these two letters spell?
A sight word that we all know well —
Up, up, up!

Sight Word Tales

A Book With a Pig

by Maria Fleming
illustrated by Doug Jones

THE THREE LITTLE PIGS

Sight Words

Sight words are words that you see again and again when you read. This story is filled with the sight words **was**, **not**, **a**, and **with**. Look for them in the text. Check the pictures, too!

I fell out of **a** book. Which book **was** it?

It **was not a** book **with a** glass slipper.

It **was not** a book **with a** candy house.

It **was** **not a** book **with a** giant.

It **was not a** book **with a** spider.

It **was not a** book **with a** cookie.

It **was not a** book **with a** troll.

It **was not a** book **with** bears.

It **WAS** a book **with** pigs...

...and **a** wolf. RUN!!!

Wow! That **was a** close call!
He **was not a** very nice wolf.

But this is **a** very nice home!

Sight Word Review

Do you know the four sight words in this story?
Read aloud the word on each cover.

with   not   a   was

not   was   with   a

134

Sight Word Fill-ins

Listen to the sentences. Then choose a sight word from the box to fill in each blank.

> **Word Box**   **was**   **not**   **a**   **with**

1. He did _____ want to go to the doctor.

2. My dog came _____ us to the park.

3. We read _____ book about bears.

4. Will you play _____ me?

5. She _____ sick yesterday.

6. Do _____ start the game yet.

7. The movie _____ very funny.

8. May I borrow _____ pencil?

Sight Word Cheers

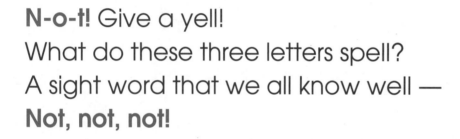

Celebrate the new sight words you learned by saying these four short cheers.

W-a-s! Give a yell!
What do these three letters spell?
A sight word that we all know well —
Was, was, was!

N-o-t! Give a yell!
What do these three letters spell?
A sight word that we all know well —
Not, not, not!

A! Give a yell!
What does this one letter spell?
A sight word that we all know well —
A, a, a!

W-i-t-h! Give a yell!
What do these four letters spell?
A sight word that we all know well —
With, with, with!

Sight Word Tales ™

Don't Be Afraid, Monster

by Maria Fleming
illustrated by Mike Moran

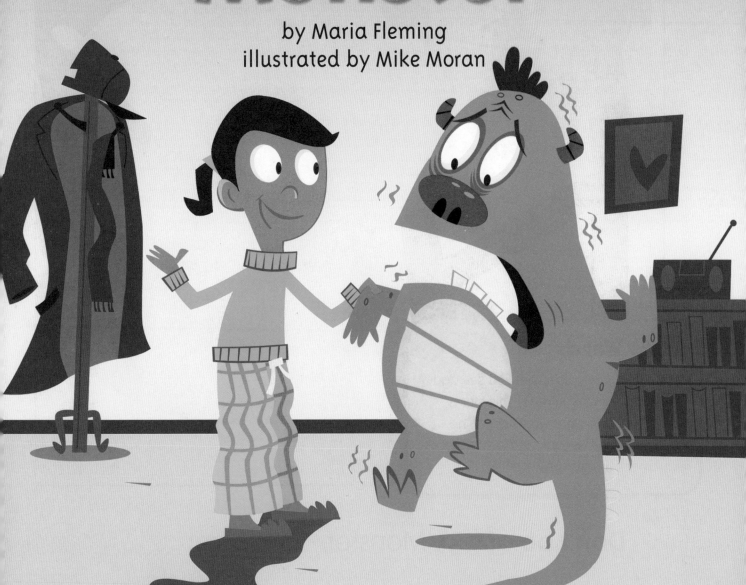

Sight Words

Sight words are words that you see again and again when you read. This story is filled with the sight words **don't, be, there,** and **under.** Look for them in the text. Check the pictures, too!

Don't be afraid, Monster.

138

There is nothing scary **under** the blanket.

Don't be afraid, Monster.

There is nothing scary **under** the desk.

Don't be afraid, Monster.

There is nothing scary **under** the coat.

Don't be afraid, Monster.

There is nothing scary **under** the towel.

Don't be afraid, Monster.

There is nothing scary **under** the bed.

Time to go to sleep, Monster.

Sweet dreams **under there**!

Sight Word Review

Do you know the four sight words in this story? Read aloud the word on each pillow.

150

Sight Word Fill-ins

Listen to the sentences. Then choose a sight word from the box to fill in each blank.

Word Box	**don't**	**be**	**there**	**under**

1 You can _____ so silly!

2 They _____ want to go.

3 The crayons are over _____.

4 My shoe was _____ the bed.

5 We _____ need our coats today.

6 Are _____ any more apples?

7 The ball rolled _____ the bush.

8 I have to _____ home by noon.

Answers: 1. be 2. don't 3. there 4. under 5. don't 6. there 7. under 8. be

Sight Word Cheers

Celebrate the new sight words you learned by saying these four short cheers.

D-o-n'-t! Give a yell!
What do these four letters spell?
A sight word that we all know well —
Don't, don't, don't!

B-e! Give a yell!
What do these two letters spell?
A sight word that we all know well —
Be, be, be!

T-h-e-r-e! Give a yell!
What do these five letters spell?
A sight word that we all know well —
There, there, there!

U-n-d-e-r! Give a yell!
What do these five letters spell?
A sight word that we all know well —
Under, under, under!

Sight Word Tales™

does want
yes say

Does Polly Want a Cracker?

by Jane Quinn

illustrated by Patrick Girouard

Sight Words

Sight words are words that you see again and again when you read. This story is filled with the sight words **does**, **want**, **yes**, and **say**. Look for them in the text. Check the pictures, too!

Polly is hungry. **Does** Polly **want** a cracker?
Yes! Polly **does want** a cracker!

Say the magic word, Polly.
But Polly **does** not remember it.

Does Polly **want** an apple?
Yes! Polly **does want** an apple!

Say the magic word, Polly.
But Polly **does** not remember it.

Does Polly **want** a sandwich?
Yes! Polly **does want** a sandwich!

Say the magic word, Polly.
But Polly **does** not remember it.

Does Polly **want** a cupcake?
Yes! Polly **does want** a cupcake!

Say the magic word, Polly.
Polly thinks and thinks.

"PLEASE!" Polly **says**.

Polly **does** remember it! She **does**!

Then she **says**, "Polly **wants** a sandwich,
PLEASE!"

"Polly **wants** an apple, PLEASE!
Polly **wants** a cracker, PLEASE!"

And Polly even remembers to **say**,
"Thank you!"

Sight Word Review

Do you know the four sight words in this story?
Read aloud the word on each apple.

does

want

want

say

yes

yes

does

say

Sight Word Fill-ins

does want
yes   say

Listen to the sentences. Then choose a sight word from the box to fill in each blank.

Word Box   **does   want   yes   say**

1 Where _____ this bus go?

2 I _____ to read this book.

3 It is nice to _____ "please" and "thank you."

4 Is the answer _____ or *no*?

5 They _____ "hello" to us every morning.

6 She _____ not like rainy days.

7 We _____ to get a puppy.

8 I always say "_____" to ice cream.

Sight Word Cheers

Celebrate the new sight words you learned by saying these four short cheers.

D-o-e-s! Give a yell!
What do these four letters spell?
A sight word that we all know well —
Does, does, does!

W-a-n-t! Give a yell!
What do these four letters spell?
A sight word that we all know well —
Want, want, want!

Y-e-s! Give a yell!
What do these three letters spell?
A sight word that we all know well —
Yes, yes, yes!

S-a-y! Give a yell!
What do these three letters spell?
A sight word that we all know well —
Say, say, say!

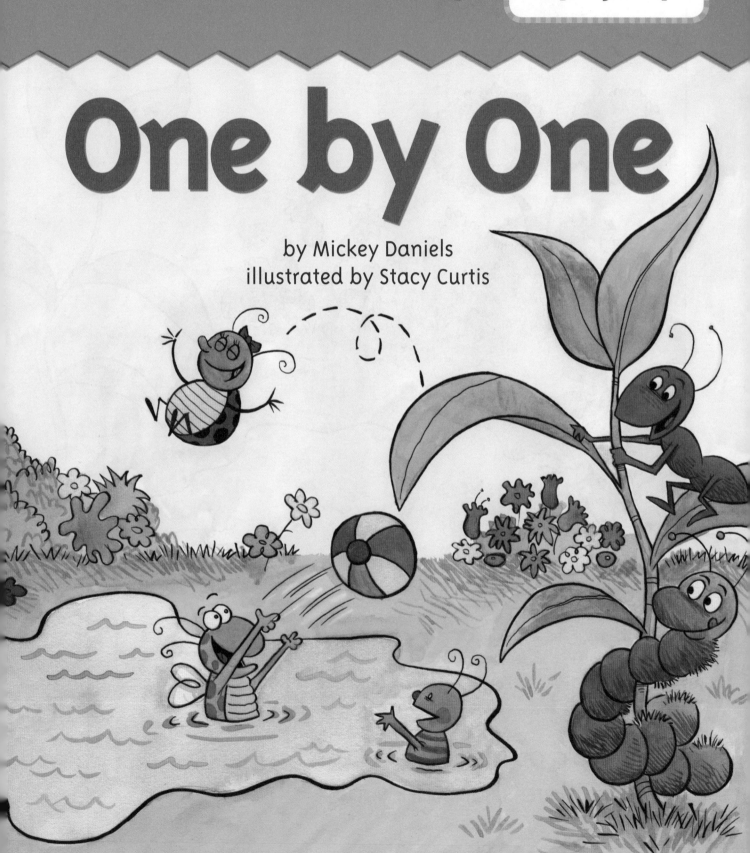

Sight Word Tales™

in   one
by   jump

One by One

by Mickey Daniels
illustrated by Stacy Curtis

The rain passed **by**.
Now there's sun, sun, sun!

The bugs are ready
for some puddle-**jump** fun!

There goes ladybug!
Oh, what fun!

The bugs **jump in,
one by one.**

There goes ant!
Oh, what fun!

The bugs **jump in,
one by one**.

There goes caterpillar!
Oh, what fun!

The bugs **jump in,**
one by one.

There goes frog. Oh, no, no, no!
The bugs **jump** out and go, go, go —

all at once,
not **one by one**.

And that's the end
of their puddle-**jump** fun....

Until they find another **one**!

Sight Word Review

Do you know the four sight words in this story? Read aloud the word on each puddle.

182

Sight Word Fill-ins

Listen to the sentences. Then choose a
sight word from the box to fill in each blank.

Word Box   **in   one   by   jump**

1 Frogs can _____ very far.

2 I did it all _____ myself!

3 Fish live _____ the ocean.

4 He gave his dog _____ bone.

5 Put the pie _____ the oven to bake.

6 We had a picnic _____ the lake.

7 Do not _____ on the bed!

8 I have _____ sister.

Answers: 1. jump 2. by 3. in 4. one 5. in 6. by 7. jump 8. one

183

Sight Word Cheers

Celebrate the new sight words you learned by saying these four short cheers.

I-n! Give a yell!
What do these two letters spell?
A sight word that we all know well —
In, in, in!

O-n-e! Give a yell!
What do these three letters spell?
A sight word that we all know well —
One, one, one!

B-y! Give a yell!
What do these two letters spell?
A sight word that we all know well —
By, by, by!

J-u-m-p! Give a yell!
What do these four letters spell?
A sight word that we all know well —
Jump, jump, jump!

How Do You Make a Giraffe Laugh?

by Catherine Bittner

illustrated by Kelly Kennedy

How do you **make** a giraffe **laugh**?
Tickle his knees? No.

How do you **make** a giraffe **laugh**?
Juggle some peas? No.

How do you make a giraffe laugh?
Make balloon hats? No.

How do you **make** a giraffe **laugh**?
Dance with wombats? No.

How do you **make** a giraffe **laugh**?
Balance some fruit? No.

How **do** you **make** a giraffe **laugh**?
Wear an ape suit? No.

How do you **make** a giraffe **laugh**?
Hang upside-down? No.

How do you **make** a giraffe **laugh**?
Dress like a clown? No.

How do you **make** a giraffe **laugh**?
Act like a kangaroo? No.

How do you **make** a giraffe **laugh**?
Tell a joke or two? Yes!

Look at that giraffe **laugh** and **laugh**
and **laugh** till he cries!

Congratulations! You win the prize!

Sight Word Review

Do you know the four sight words in this story?
Read aloud the word on each balloon.

Sight Word Fill-ins

Listen to the sentences. Then choose a sight word from the box to fill in each blank.

> **Word Box**   **how**   **do**   **make**   **laugh**

1 Her dog can _____ tricks.

2 Please show us _____ to play the game.

3 That funny story made me _____.

4 Can you _____ a giraffe from clay?

5 I know _____ to ice-skate.

6 They _____ not live near us.

7 He will _____ soup for dinner.

8 I always _____ at clowns.

Sight Word Cheers

Celebrate the new sight words you learned by saying these four short cheers.

H-o-w! Give a yell!
What do these three letters spell?
A sight word that we all know well —
How, how, how!

D-o! Give a yell!
What do these two letters spell?
A sight word that we all know well —
Do, do, do!

M-a-k-e! Give a yell!
What do these four letters spell?
A sight word that we all know well —
Make, make, make!

L-a-u-g-h! Give a yell!
What do these five letters spell?
A sight word that we all know well —
Laugh, laugh, laugh!

Sight Word Tales™

shall bring
him   or

What Shall I Bring the King?

by Maria Fleming

illustrated by John Manders

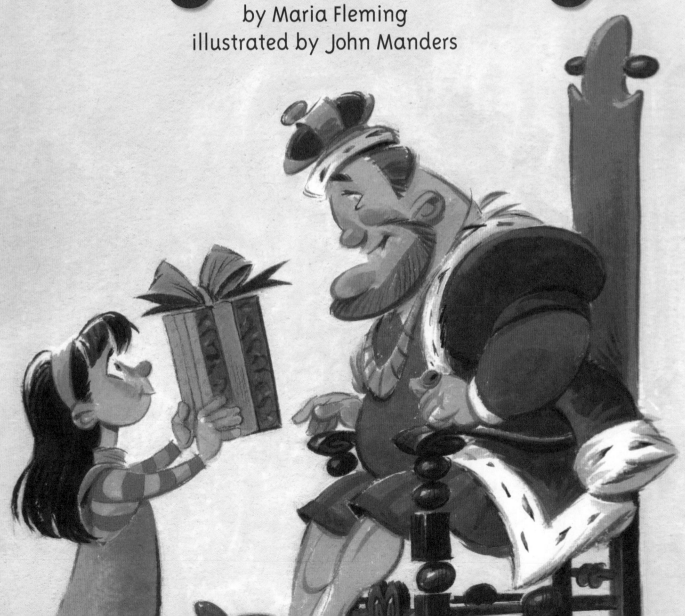

Happy birthday to the king!
There's a party for **him**.
What **shall** I **bring**?

202

Shall I **bring him** a jump rope
or a hula-hoop?

Shall I bring him a plane
that can loop-de-loop?

Shall I **bring him** a yo-yo **or** a jack-in-the-box?

Shall I **bring him** pajamas
or slippers **or** socks?

Or do kings have closets full of these things?

I **shall bring him** something
he does not have for sure.
I **shall bring him** a unicorn!

Or a dinosaur!

Or a flock of peacocks!

Or a magical elf!

I know what I **shall bring** the king!

May your birthday **bring** you happiness.

May your birthday **bring** you sun.

May your birthday **bring** you friends.

May your birthday **bring** you fun.

No rubies **or** gold **or** diamonds,

Or fancy gifts **shall** do.

No, none of these can measure

How much we all love you!

I shall bring him a poem
that I write myself!

Sight Word Review

Do you know the four sight words in this story?
Read aloud the word on each gift box.

shall

him

bring

or

or

shall

him

bring

214

Sight Word Fill-ins

Listen to the sentences. Then choose a sight word from the box to fill in each blank.

Word Box   **shall**   **bring**   **him**   **or**

1 The teacher asked _____ a question.

2 I _____ not give up!

3 They will paint it blue _____ green.

4 We gave _____ a present.

5 She will _____ a gift to the party.

6 Do you have a cat _____ a dog?

7 Please _____ me that book.

8 What _____ we do today?

Sight Word Cheers

Celebrate the new sight words you learned by saying these four short cheers.

S-h-a-l-l! Give a yell!
What do these five letters spell?
A sight word that we all know well —
Shall, shall, shall!

B-r-i-n-g! Give a yell!
What do these five letters spell?
A sight word that we all know well —
Bring, bring, bring!

H-i-m! Give a yell!
What do these three letters spell?
A sight word that we all know well —
Him, him, him!

O-r! Give a yell!
What do these two letters spell?
A sight word that we all know well —
Or, or, or!

Sight Word Tales ™

The Penguins Are Going on Vacation

by Catherine Bittner

illustrated by Doug Jones

Sight Words

Sight words are words that you see again and again when you read. This story is filled with the sight words **are**, **going**, **they**, and **play**. Look for them in the text. Check the pictures, too!

The penguins **are going** on vacation.

They are going to **play** and have fun.

They are going to **play** on the beach.

They are going to **play** in the sun.

They are going to play in the sand.

They are going to **play** in the trees.

They are going to **play** on surfboards.

They are going to **play** on skis.

The penguins **are going** on vacation.

The penguins **are going** to pack.

They are sure **they are going** to have fun.

They are NOT sure **they are going**
to come back!

Sight Word Review

Do you know the four sight words in this story?
Read aloud the word on each pail.

Sight Word Fill-ins

Listen to the sentences. Then choose a sight word from the box to fill in each blank.

Word Box	**are**	**going**	**they**	**play**

1 He is _____ to the beach.

2 Let's _____ in the park.

3 When will _____ be back from vacation?

4 My brothers _____ older than me.

5 I am _____ to the baseball game.

6 We _____ writing stories today.

7 She loves to _____ soccer.

8 Can _____ come with us?

Answers: 1. going 2. play 3. they 4. are 5. going 6. are 7. play 8. they

231

Sight Word Cheers

Celebrate the new sight words you learned by saying these four short cheers.

A-r-e! Give a yell!
What do these three letters spell?
A sight word that we all know well —
Are, are, are!

G-o-i-n-g! Give a yell!
What do these five letters spell?
A sight word that we all know well —
Going, going, going!

T-h-e-y! Give a yell!
What do these four letters spell?
A sight word that we all know well —
They, they, they!

P-l-a-y! Give a yell!
What do these four letters spell?
A sight word that we all know well —
Play, play, play!

Sight Word Tales ™

Some Dogs Are Very Good

by Mickey Daniels
illustrated by Richard Torrey

Sight Words

Sight words are words that you see again and again when you read. This story is filled with the sight words **some**, **very**, **good**, and **but**. Look for them in the text. Check the pictures, too!

Some dogs are **very good** at doing tricks.

But not Spot.

Some dogs are **very good**
at fetching sticks.

But not Spot.

Some dogs are **very good** at staying clean and neat.

But not Spot.

Some dogs are **very good** at waiting for a treat.

But not Spot.

Some dogs are **very good**—
as **good** as **good** can be.

But not Spot.

Spot is **very good** at being Spot.

But that is **good** enough for me!

Sight Word Review

Do you know the four sight words
in this story? Read aloud
the word on each flower.

good

some

some

but

very

very

good

but

246

Sight Word Fill-ins

Listen to the sentences. Then choose a sight word from the box to fill in each blank.

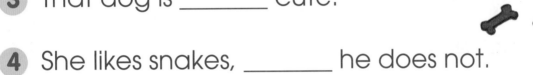

Word Box   **some**   **very**   **good**   **but**

1 This soap smells _____.

2 Try _____ of this pie.

3 That dog is _____ cute.

4 She likes snakes, _____ he does not.

5 May I borrow _____ of your paper?

6 He is _____ at spelling.

7 Everyone went outside _____ me.

8 This box is _____ big.

Answers: 1. good 2. some 3. very 4. but 5. some 6. good 7. but 8. very

247

Sight Word Cheer

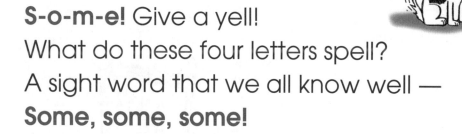

some very
good but

Celebrate the new sight words you learned by saying these four short cheers.

S-o-m-e! Give a yell!
What do these four letters spell?
A sight word that we all know well —
Some, some, some!

V-e-r-y! Give a yell!
What do these four letters spell?
A sight word that we all know well —
Very, very, very!

G-o-o-d! Give a yell!
What do these four letters spell?
A sight word that we all know well —
Good, good, good!

B-u-t! Give a yell!
What do these three letters spell?
A sight word that we all know well —
But, but, but!

Have You Seen Jellybean?

by Maria Fleming
illustrated by Amy Wummer

Sight Words

Sight words are words that you see again and again when you read. This story is filled with the sight words **have, you, ask,** and **her**. Look for them in the text. Check the pictures, too!

My hamster, Jellybean, got out of **her** cage.
I **have** to find **her**!

I **ask** my brother, "**Have you** seen Jellybean?"
"I **have** not seen **her**," my brother says.

I **ask** my sister, "**Have you** seen Jellybean?"
"I **have** not seen **her**," my sister says.

I **ask** my mother, "**Have you** seen Jellybean?"
"I **have** not seen **her**," my mother says.

I **ask** my father, "**Have you** seen Jellybean?"
"I **have** not seen **her**," my father says.

I **ask** my friend, "**Have you** seen Jellybean?"
"I **have** not seen **her**," my friend says.

I **ask** my neighbor, "**Have you** seen Jellybean?"
"I **have** not seen **her**," my neighbor says.

Oh, Jellybean! Where **have you** gone?
I miss **you** so much!

Jellybean! I **have** found **you** at last!

I **ask her**, "Where **have you** been hiding?"
Jellybean just wiggles **her** whiskers.

I put Jellybean in **her** cage.
"**You have** to rest now," I tell **her**.

She closes **her** eyes. Good night, Jellybean.
I hope **you have** dreams as sweet as **you**!

Sight Word Review

Do you know the four sight words in this story?
Read aloud the word on each teacup.

have

ask

you

her

her

have

ask

you

Sight Word Fill-ins

Listen to the sentences. Then choose a sight word from the box to fill in each blank.

> **Word Box**   **have**   **you**   **ask**   **her**

1 She lost _____ mitten.

2 May I _____ some popcorn?

3 Do _____ walk to school?

4 They _____ us for help.

5 This is _____ favorite book.

6 Can _____ come over today?

7 We _____ two cats.

8 I _____ the teacher a question.

Answers: 1. her 2. have 3. you 4. you 5. her 6. you 7. have 8. ask

263

Sight Word Cheers

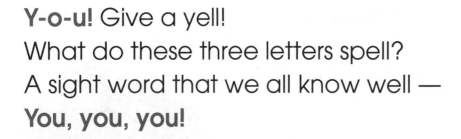

have you
ask her

Celebrate the new sight words you learned by saying these four short cheers.

H-a-v-e! Give a yell!
What do these four letters spell?
A sight word that we all know well —
Have, have, have!

Y-o-u! Give a yell!
What do these three letters spell?
A sight word that we all know well —
You, you, you!

A-s-k! Give a yell!
What do these three letters spell?
A sight word that we all know well —
Ask, ask, ask!

H-e-r! Give a yell!
What do these three letters spell?
A sight word that we all know well —
Her, her, her!

Sight Word Tales ™

All Puffins Just Love Muffins

by Jane Quinn
illustrated by Bill Dare

Sight Words

Sight words are words that you see again and again when you read. This story is filled with the sight words **help**, **them**, **all**, and **just**. Look for them in the text. Check the pictures, too!

Just look at **all** the hungry puffins —
dreaming **all** day long of muffins.

They need somebody, maybe you,
to **help them** bake a batch or two.

Help them choose a recipe.
All puffins just love muffins!

Help them measure carefully.
All puffins just love muffins!

Help them add the eggs — **just** a few.
All puffins **just** love muffins!

Help them add the flour, too.
All puffins **just** love muffins!

Help them mix the berries in.
All puffins **just** love muffins!

Help them fill each muffin tin.
All puffins just love muffins!

Just one more thing for **them** to do —

all by themselves, no **help** from you. . .

Time for **them** to EAT THE MUFFINS!
And, as you can tell,
all the puffins do this well.

Because. . .
all puffins **just** love muffins!

Sight Word Review

Do you know the four sight words in this story? Read aloud the word on each muffin.

them

just

help

all

help

all

them

just

Sight Word Fill-ins

Listen to the sentences. Then choose a
sight word from the box to fill in each blank.

Word Box   help   them   all   just

1 I can _____ you tie your shoes.

2 She _____ loves that movie!

3 Where did you put _____?

4 We gave _____ of the puppies away.

5 He likes to _____ his mom rake leaves.

6 I had _____ one cookie.

7 Their teacher took _____ to the museum.

8 Where did _____ of the ducks go?

Answers: 1. help 2. just 3. them 4. all 5. help 6. just 7. them 8. all

Sight Word Cheers

Celebrate the new sight words you learned by saying these four short cheers.

H-e-l-p! Give a yell!
What do these four letters spell?
A sight word that we all know well —
Help, help, help!

T-h-e-m! Give a yell!
What do these four letters spell?
A sight word that we all know well —
Them, them, them!

A-l-l! Give a yell!
What do these three letters spell?
A sight word that we all know well —
All, all, all!

J-u-s-t! Give a yell!
What do these four letters spell?
A sight word that we all know well —
Just, just, just!

Today Is So Boring!

by Catherine Bittner
illustrated by Doug Jones

Oh, **today** is **as** boring **as** boring can be.
There's nothing **today** to do or see.

282

It's **so** dull **today**. It's **so** totally boring.
I might **as well** be snoozing and snoring.

I might **as well** just stare at the sky.
I might **as well** watch the clouds drift by.

Today is **so** boring.
I just feel like snoring.

I might **as well** count each blade of grass.
I might **as well** count the ants **as** they pass.

Today is **so** boring.
I just feel like snoring.

I might **as well** watch a dull TV show.
I might **as well** watch my fingernails grow.

288

Today is **so** boring.
I just feel like snoring.

I might **as well** just stare at the clock.
I might **as well** count each tick and tock.

Today is **so** boring.
I just feel like snoring.

I might **as well** go to bed early **today**.
Oh, **today** was **so** boring in every way.

I might **as well** snooze. I might **as well** snore.
I just hope tomorrow won't be such a bore!

Sight Word Review

Do you know the four sight words in this story?
Read aloud the word on each bubble.

today

as

well

so

well

so

as

today

294

Sight Word Fill-ins

Listen to the sentences. Then choose a
sight word from the box to fill in each blank.

Word Box	today	so	as	well

1 That puppy is _____ cute!

2 They went to the park _____.

3 She dressed up _____ a fairy for the play.

4 Will _____ be hot or cold?

5 Our teacher is not feeling _____.

6 We worked _____ a team on the project.

7 I am _____ happy to see you!

8 He plays the piano very _____.

Answers: 1. so 2. today 3. as 4. today 5. well 6. as 7. so 8. well

295

Sight Word Cheers

Celebrate the new sight words you learned by saying these four short cheers.

T-o-d-a-y! Give a yell!
What do these five letters spell?
A sight word that we all know well —
Today, today, today!

S-o! Give a yell!
What do these two letters spell?
A sight word that we all know well —
So, so, so!

A-s! Give a yell!
What do these two letters spell?
A sight word that we all know well —
As, as, as!

W-e-l-l! Give a yell!
What do these four letters spell?
A sight word that we all know well —
Well, well, well!

Sight Word Tales™

many kind
which buy

So Many Kinds of Shoes!

by Maria Fleming
illustrated by Beccy Blake

Spider needs to **buy** new shoes.
Which kind of shoes will Spider choose?

Will she **buy** the **kind** for running races?

Or maybe
I will **buy** this **kind**.

Will she **buy** the **kind** with purple laces?

So **many** different **kinds** of shoes!
Which kind of shoes will Spider choose?

Will she **buy** the **kind** to dance ballet?

Will she **buy** the **kind** for a rainy day?

So **many** different **kinds** of shoes!
Which kind of shoes will Spider choose?

Will she **buy** the **kind** with noisy taps?

This **kind** of shoe is fancy!

Will she **buy** the **kind** with flowered straps?

So **many** different **kinds** of shoes!
Which kind of shoes will Spider choose?

Many shoes, but **many** feet.
Many feet just can't be beat!

Spider has made up her mind.
She **buys** one of every **kind**!

Sight Word Review

Do you know the four sight words in this story?
Read aloud the word on each shoe.

many

buy

many   kind   which

which   buy   kind

310

Sight Word Fill-ins

**Listen to the sentences. Then choose a
sight word from the box to fill in each blank.**

Word Box   **many**   **which**   **kind**   **buy**

1 He has _____ friends.

2 Tell me _____ one you want.

3 What _____ of dog is that?

4 We went to the store to _____ milk.

5 How _____ pennies are in the jar?

6 Vanilla is her favorite _____ of ice cream.

7 He will _____ new sneakers today.

8 I don't know _____ way to go.

Answers: 1. many 2. which 3. kind 4. buy 5. many 6. kind 7. buy 8. which

Sight Word Cheers

Celebrate the new sight words you learned by saying these four short cheers.

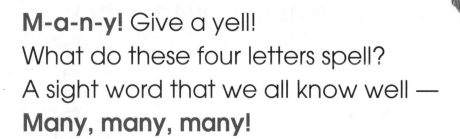

M-a-n-y! Give a yell!
What do these four letters spell?
A sight word that we all know well —
Many, many, many!

W-h-i-c-h! Give a yell!
What do these five letters spell?
A sight word that we all know well —
Which, which, which!

K-i-n-d! Give a yell!
What do these four letters spell?
A sight word that we all know well —
Kind, kind, kind!

B-u-y! Give a yell!
What do these three letters spell?
A sight word that we all know well —
Buy, buy, buy!

Sight Word Tales ™

who   would
these   funny

Who Would Buy These Clothes?

by Catherine Bittner
illustrated by Richard Torrey

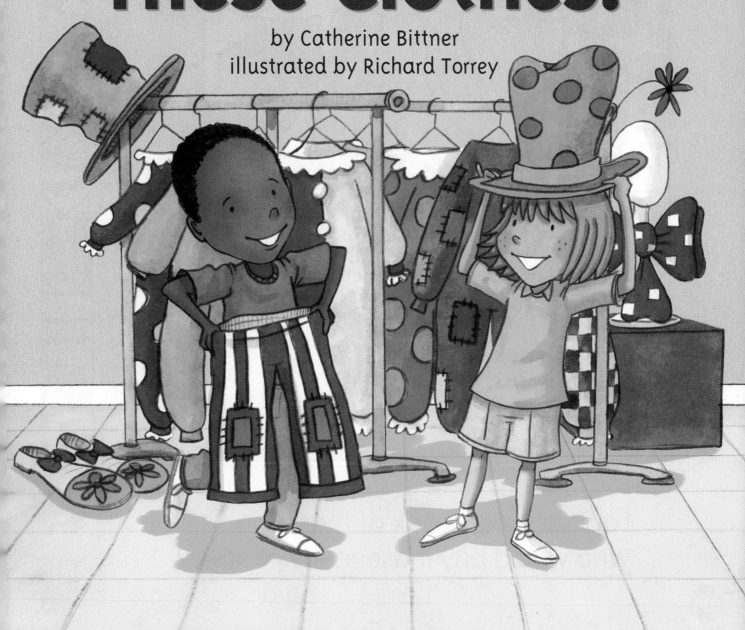

Sight Words

Sight words are words that you see again and again when you read. This story is filled with the sight words **who**, **would**, **these**, and **funny**. Look for them in the text. Check the pictures, too!

Look at **these**! Look at those!
Who would buy **these funny** clothes?

Who would buy **these funny** pants?

Who would buy **these funny** shirts?

Who would buy **these funny** ties?

Who would buy **these funny** skirts?

Who would buy **these funny** shoes?
Who would buy **these funny** boots?

Who would buy **these funny** hats?

Who would buy **these funny** suits?

Who would buy **these funny** wigs?

Who would buy **these funny** gowns?

Oh! That's **who would** buy **these funny** clothes...

clowns!

Sight Word Review

Do you know the four sight words in this story? Read aloud the word on each hat.

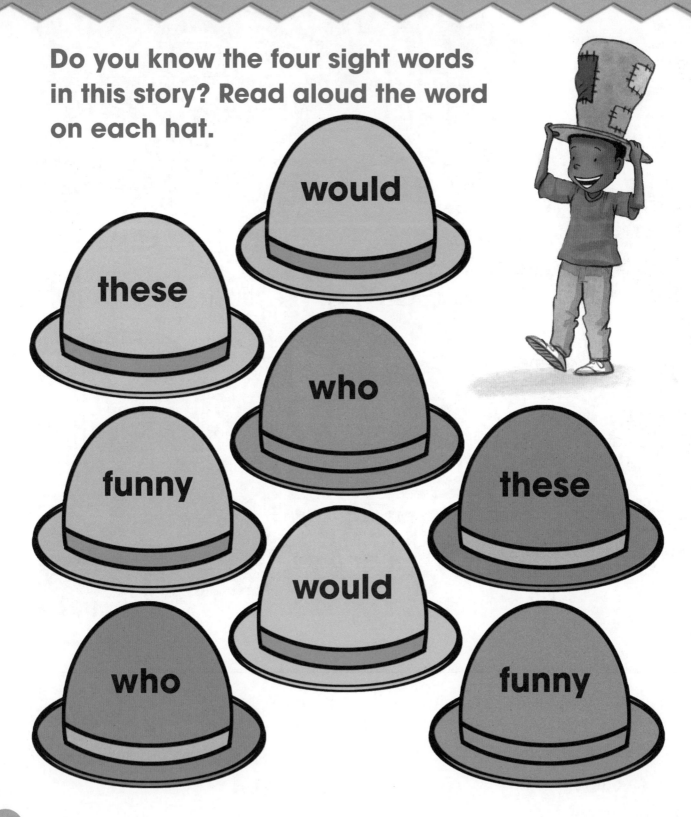

would

these

who

funny

these

who

would

funny

326

Sight Word Fill-ins

Listen to the sentences. Then choose a sight word from the box to fill in each blank.

Word Box	**who**	**would**	**these**	**funny**

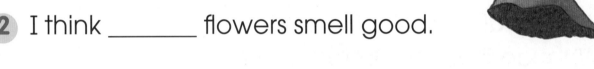

1 We read a _____ book.

2 I think _____ flowers smell good.

3 Do you know _____ drew this picture?

4 They _____ not go home.

5 That joke was very _____.

6 Where should I put _____?

7 Guess _____ won the prize!

8 She _____ like to come with us.

Sight Word Cheers

Celebrate the new sight words you learned by saying these four short cheers.

W-h-o! Give a yell!
What do these three letters spell?
A sight word that we all know well —
Who, who, who!

W-o-u-l-d! Give a yell!
What do these five letters spell?
A sight word that we all know well —
Would, would, would!

T-h-e-s-e! Give a yell!
What do these five letters spell?
A sight word that we all know well —
These, these, these!

F-u-n-n-y! Give a yell!
What do these five letters spell?
A sight word that we all know well —
Funny, funny, funny!

Sight Word Tales™

try again
fall down

Try Again, Hen!

by Jane Quinn
illustrated by Franfou

Sight Words

Sight words are words that you see again and again when you read. This story is filled with the sight words **try**, **again**, **fall**, and **down**. Look for them in the text. Check the pictures, too!

Hen has a new skateboard.
She wants to **try** to ride it.

"I hope I don't **fall**," says Hen.
She hops on and rolls **down** the road.

SLOP! Hen **falls** in the mud.
"**Try again**, Hen!" says Pig.

I will **try** not to **fall down again**.

Hen rolls **down** the road **again**.

FLOP! Hen **falls** in the hay.
"**Try again**, Hen!" says Sheep.

Hen rolls **down** the road **again**.

PLOP! Hen **falls** in the pond.

"**Try again**, Hen!" says Duck.

Hen rolls **down** the road **again**.
Down, down, down she rolls.

Hen does not **fall** in the mud. She does not **fall** in the hay. She does not **fall** in the pond.

Hen does not **fall** at all!
"Hooray for Hen!" the animals shout.

"May we **try** to ride your skateboard?"
Pig, Sheep, and Duck ask Hen.

"Of course you may **try**," says Hen.
And they do—**again** and **again** and **again**!

Sight Word Review

Do you know the four sight words in this story? Read aloud the word on each skateboard.

again

try

fall

down

try

again

down

fall

Sight Word Fill-ins

Listen to the sentences. Then choose a
sight word from the box to fill in each blank.

Word Box   try   again   fall   down

1 I will _____ to hit the ball.

2 May we go to the museum _____?

3 The leaves _____ off the trees in autumn.

4 They rode their bikes _____ the hill.

5 She will _____ to spell the word.

6 The cat climbed _____ the stairs.

7 I want to see that movie _____!

8 We watched snow _____ from the sky.

Answers: 1. try 2. again 3. fall 4. down 5. try 6. up 7. again 8. fall

343

Sight Word Cheers

Celebrate the new sight words you learned by saying these four short cheers.

T-r-y! Give a yell!
What do these three letters spell?
A sight word that we all know well —
Try, try, try!

A-g-a-i-n! Give a yell!
What do these five letters spell?
A sight word that we all know well —
Again, again, again!

F-a-l-l! Give a yell!
What do these four letters spell?
A sight word that we all know well —
Fall, fall, fall!

D-o-w-n! Give a yell!
What do these four letters spell?
A sight word that we all know well —
Down, down, down!

Sight Word Tales ™

Let's Make Soup Together

by Mickey Daniels

illustrated by Mike Gordon

Sight Words

Sight words are words that you see again and again when you read. This story is filled with the sight words **take, together, then,** and **around**. Look for them in the text. Check the pictures, too!

Gather **around**, one and all.
Let's cook up some fun.

Together, we'll make silly soup.
Take a look at how it's done.

Take soda pop.
Take one pork chop.
Take pickles — quite a lot.

Mix them all **together**,
then skip **around** the pot.

Take squishy peas.
Take stinky cheese.
Take oatmeal — quite a lot.

Mix them all **together**,
then march **around** the pot.

Take macaroni.
Take old baloney.
Take jelly — quite a lot.

Mix them all **together**,
then dance **around** the pot.

Take jellybeans.
Take tangerines.
Take mustard — quite a lot.

Mix them all **together**,
then it's time to heat the pot.

For silly fun **together**,
no soup **around** can beat it.

Silly soup is soup-er fun —
until you have to eat it!

Sight Word Review

Do you know the four sight words in this story?
Read aloud the word on each bowl.

together

take

around

then

together

take

then

around

358

Sight Word Fill-ins

Listen to the sentences. Then choose a sight word from the box to fill in each blank.

> **Word Box** take   together   then   around

1 Put on your socks, _____ put on your shoes.

2 Let's play a game _____.

3 Will you _____ me to the park?

4 He skated _____ the rink.

5 She put a puzzle _____.

6 I brushed my teeth, _____ went to bed.

7 The squirrel ran _____ the tree.

8 We can _____ turns on the swing.

359

Sight Word Cheers

Celebrate the new sight words you learned by saying these four short cheers.

T-a-k-e! Give a yell!
What do these four letters spell?
A sight word that we all know well —
Take, take, take!

T-o-g-e-t-h-e-r! Give a yell!
What do these eight letters spell?
A sight word that we all know well —
Together, together, together!

T-h-e-n! Give a yell!
What do these four letters spell?
A sight word that we all know well —
Then, then, then!

A-r-o-u-n-d! Give a yell!
What do these six letters spell?
A sight word that we all know well —
Around, around, around!

Sight Word Tales ™

please   if
stop   must

Please Stop Monkeying Around!

by Maria Fleming
illustrated by Kelly Kennedy

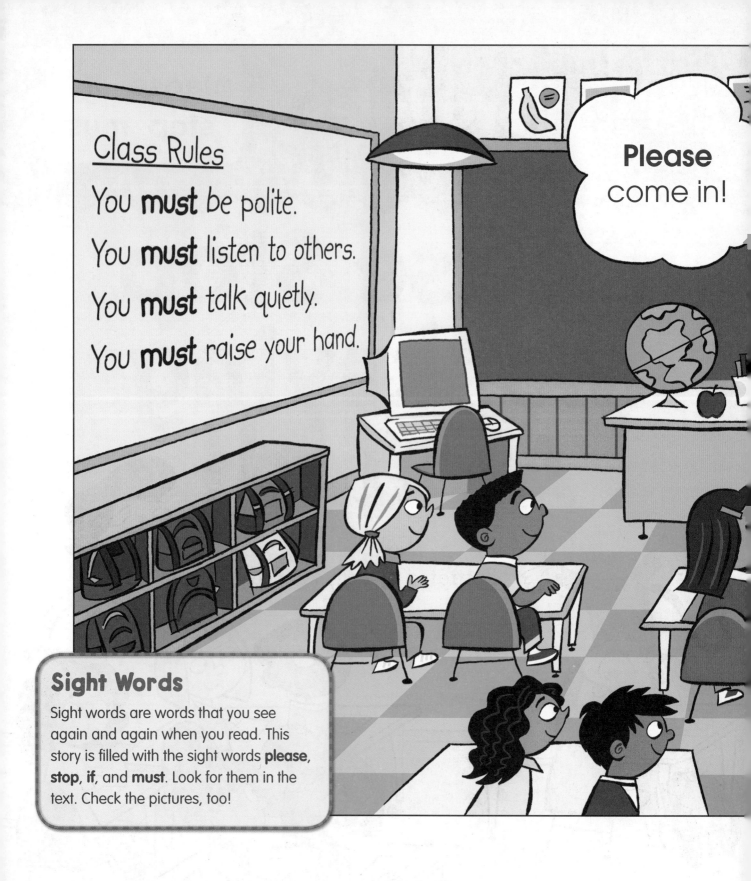

Class Rules

You **must** be polite.

You **must** listen to others.

You **must** talk quietly.

You **must** raise your hand.

Please come in!

Sight Words

Sight words are words that you see again and again when you read. This story is filled with the sight words **please**, **stop**, **if**, and **must**. Look for them in the text. Check the pictures, too!

Welcome, Monkey! **Please** come in.
We're glad that you're our guest.

But **if** you stay, you **must** behave.
Please, Monkey, do your best.

Please stop hanging upside down.
Please stop swinging to and fro.

Please stop monkeying around!
If you don't, then you **must** go.

Please stop writing on the wall.
Please stop playing tic-tac-toe.

Please stop monkeying around!
If you don't, then you **must** go.

Please stop dancing on the desk.
Please stop putting on a show.

Please stop monkeying around!
If you don't, then you **must** go.

Please stop snacking on bananas.
Please stop breaking every rule.

Please start packing up your things.
You **must** go. **Please** leave our school!

If you **must** monkey around,
you **must** do so at the zoo.

Please don't visit us again.
We would rather visit you!

Sight Word Review

Do you know the four sight words in this story?
Read aloud the word on each hat.

374

Sight Word Fill-ins

Listen to the sentences. Then choose a
sight word from the box to fill in each blank.

Word Box	please	stop	if	must

1 He _____ be very tired.

2 Ask your mom _____ you can come.

3 You _____ finish your work.

4 They will _____ by to visit.

5 Will you _____ talk quietly!

6 I can watch TV _____ I clean my room.

7 She had to _____ playing and go home.

8 May I _____ stay up late?

375

Sight Word Cheers

please if
stop must

Celebrate the new sight words you learned by saying these four short cheers.

P-l-e-a-s-e! Give a yell!
What do these six letters spell?
A sight word that we all know well —
Please, please, please!

S-t-o-p! Give a yell!
What do these four letters spell?
A sight word that we all know well —
Stop, stop, stop!

I-f! Give a yell!
What do these two letters spell?
A sight word that we all know well —
If, if, if!

M-u-s-t! Give a yell!
What do these four letters spell?
A sight word that we all know well —
Must, must, must!

Sight Word Tales ™

Little Bo-Peep's Lost-and-Found Sheep

by Jane Quinn

illustrated by Kelly Kennedy

Sight Words Fact

Sight words are words that you see again and again when you read. This story is filled with the sight words **little**, **has**, **find**, and **found**. Look for them in the text. Check the pictures, too!

Little Bo-Peep **has** lost 15 sheep.
Poor **little** lass! She must **find** them all fast!

378

She **finds** one with a spoon on the run.

She **finds** two in a very big shoe.

Little Bo-Peep **has found** three of her sheep!
But the **little** lass must **find** the rest fast.

She **finds** six on a wall made of bricks.

Little Bo-Peep **has found** nine of her sheep!
But the **little** lass must **find** the rest fast.

She **finds** three in a tub on the sea.

Little Bo-Peep **has found** 12 of her sheep!
But the **little** lass must **find** the rest fast.

She **finds** three more doing a chore.

Little Bo-Peep **has found** all 15 sheep!
She **has found** every one!
Time for a **little** fun.

The **little** lass sneaks away
to hide in some hay.

She **found** us, but we can't **find** her!

Now all of the sheep must **find Little** Bo-Peep!

Sight Word Review

Do you know the four sight words in this story?
Read aloud the word on each sheep.

Sight Word Fill-ins

Listen to the sentences. Then choose a sight word from the box to fill in each blank.

> **Word Box**   **little**   **has**   **find**   **found**

1 My sister _____ not come home yet.

2 Ladybugs are very _____.

3 They cannot _____ their mittens.

4 He _____ five dollars on the ground.

5 May I have a _____ more milk?

6 She _____ blue eyes.

7 Last week, we _____ a frog in the woods.

8 Where did you _____ that book?

Sight Word Cheers

Celebrate the new sight words you learned by saying these four short cheers.

L-i-t-t-l-e! Give a yell!
What do these six letters spell?
A sight word that we all know well —
Little, little, little!

H-a-s! Give a yell!
What do these three letters spell?
A sight word that we all know well —
Has, has, has!

F-i-n-d! Give a yell!
What do these four letters spell?
A sight word that we all know well —
Find, find, find!

F-o-u-n-d! Give a yell!
What do these five letters spell?
A sight word that we all know well —
Found, found, found!

Sight Word Tales™

Once Upon a Planet

by Mickey Daniels
illustrated by Doug Jones

Sight Words

Sight words are words that you see again and again when you read. This story is filled with the sight words **once**, **upon**, **far**, and **away**. Look for them in the text. Check the pictures, too!

Once upon a planet, near the galaxy's end, one lonely alien longed for a friend.

At least **once** a week, he flew **far away** hoping to come **upon** a friend one day.

Once upon a planet, **far, far away,**
another alien played alone every day.

At least **once** a week, he flew **far away**
hoping to come **upon** a friend one day.

Once upon two planets, **away** so **far**,
the two wished **upon** the very same star.

They both wished for a friend,
who wanted to play
upon planets near and **far, far away**.

Then, **once upon** a planet, **far, far away,**

both aliens landed the very same day.

And **upon** that planet, **far away** from the sun,

those aliens met and had tons of fun!

Once upon a planet, near the galaxy's end,

two lonely aliens each found a friend!

Sight Word Review

Do you know the four sight words in this story?
Read aloud the word on each star.

upon

far

once

upon

once

away

far

away

Sight Word Fill-ins

Listen to the sentences. Then choose a sight word from the box to fill in each blank.

Word Box	once	upon	far	away

1 The frog sat _____ the lily pad.

2 Please put _____ your crayons.

3 How _____ can you run?

4 The cat climbed _____ my lap.

5 Please come here at _____ !

6 We rode our bikes very _____ today.

7 He threw _____ his broken toys.

8 They all yelled "Surprise!" at _____.

Answers: 1. upon 2. away 3. far 4. upon 5. once 6. far 7. away 8. once

407

Sight Word Cheers

Celebrate the new sight words you learned by saying these four short cheers.

O-n-c-e! Give a yell!
What do these four letters spell?
A sight word that we all know well —
Once, once, once!

U-p-o-n! Give a yell!
What do these four letters spell?
A sight word that we all know well —
Upon, upon, upon!

F-a-r! Give a yell!
What do these three letters spell?
A sight word that we all know well —
Far, far, far!

A-w-a-y! Give a yell!
What do these four letters spell?
A sight word that we all know well —
Away, away, away!